PRETEND YOU'RE A CAT

By JEAN MARZOLLO

Pictures by JERRY PINKNEY

SCHOLASTIC INC.
New York Toronto London Auckland Sydney

The full-color artwork was prepared using pencil, colored pencils, and watercolor. It was then color-separated and reproduced as red, blue, yellow, and black halftones.

Typographic design by Jane Byers Bierhorst

ISBN 0-590-12704-7

12 11 10 9 8 7 6 5 4 3 2 1   7 8 9/9 0 1 2/0

Printed in the U.S.A.   24

Can you climb?
Can you leap?
Can you stretch?
Can you sleep?

Can you hiss?
Can you scat?
Can you purr
Like a cat?

What else can you do like a cat?

Can you bark?
Can you beg?
Can you scratch
With your leg?

Can you fetch?
Can you roll?
Can you dig
In a hole?

What else can you do like a dog?

Can you jump?
Can you leap?
Can you swim
As you sleep?

Can you nibble
And look
At a worm
On a hook?

What else can you do like a fish?

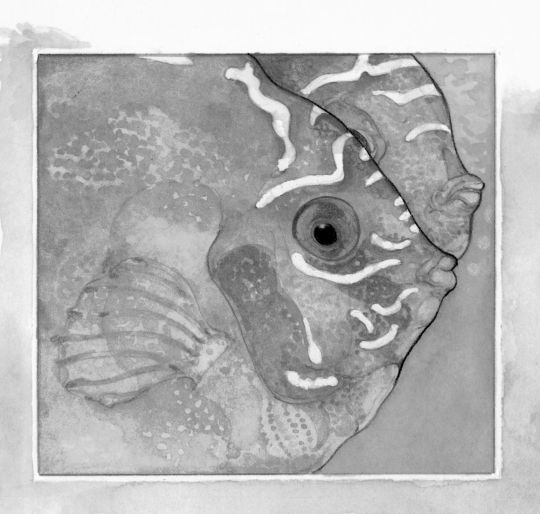

Can you fly?
Can you buzz?
Are you covered
With fuzz?

Can you land
On my knee?
Can you sting
Like a bee?

What else can you do like a bee?

Can you peck?
Can you pick
At a shell
Like a chick?

Can you scratch?
Can you cheep?
Can you hop?
Can you peep?

What else can you do like a chick?

Can you perch?
Can you fly?
Can you soar
In the sky?

Can you chirp?
Can you tweet?
Can you sing
With a beat?

What else can you do like a bird?

Can you chatter
And flee?
Disappear
In a tree?

Can you run?
Can you twirl?
Can you leap
Like a squirrel?

What else can you do like a squirrel?

Are you pink
As a bud?
Can you lie
In the mud?

Can you root?
Can you dig?
Can you snort
Like a pig?

What else can you do like a pig?

Can you chew?
Can you munch?
Can you moo
During lunch?

Can you drink
from a pail?
Touch your ear
With your tail?

What else can you do like a cow?

Can you snort?
Can you neigh?
Can you eat
Grain and hay?

Can you open
The gate?
Can you run
With your mate?

What else can you do like a horse?

Can you balance
A ball
On your nose
And not fall?

Can you dive
For your meal?
Can you bark
Like a seal?

What else can you do like a seal?

Can you wiggle
And glide?
Can you slither
And slide?

Can you head
For the lake?
Can you swim
Like a snake?

What else can you do like a snake?

Are you big?
Are you brave?
Can you sleep
In a cave?

Can you sniff
At the air?
Can you roar
Like a bear?

What else can you do like a bear?

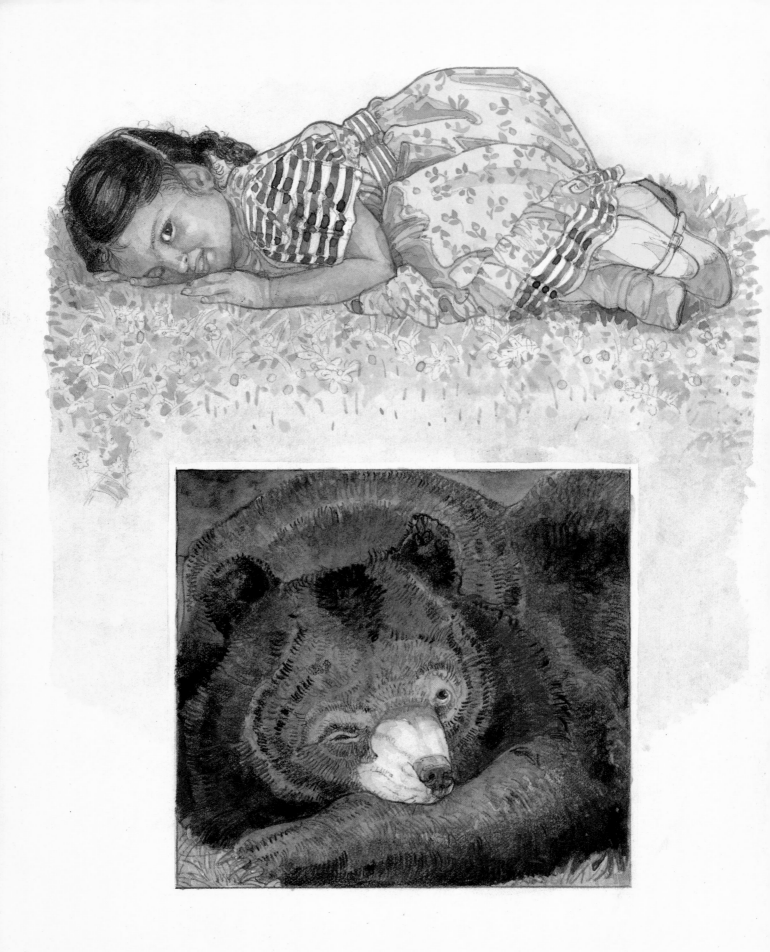